G000060160

**Official Charts Company**

# THE MILLION SELLERS

**Wise Publications**
part of The Music Sales Group
London/New York/Paris/Sydney/Copenhagen/Berlin/Madrid/Hong Kong/Tokyo

Published by
**Wise Publications**
14-15 Berners Street,
London W1T 3LJ, UK.

Exclusive Distributors:
**Music Sales Limited**
Distribution Centre, Newmarket Road,
Bury St Edmunds, Suffolk IP33 3YB, UK.
**Music Sales Corporation**
180 Madison Avenue, 24th Floor,
New York NY 10016, USA.
**Music Sales Pty Limited**
Units 3-4, 17 Willfox Street, Condell Park
NSW 2200, Australia.

Order No. AM1005664
ISBN 978-1-78038-779-6

This book © Copyright 2012 Wise Publications,
a division of Music Sales Limited.

Unauthorised reproduction of any part of this
publication by any means including photocopying is an
infringement of copyright.

Edited by Jenni Norey.
Cover design by Stuart Hammersley, Art Science.
Photographs courtesy Getty Images & Corbis Images.
Introduction by Martin Talbot.

Printed in the EU.

**Your Guarantee of Quality**
As publishers, we strive to produce every book to the
highest commercial standards.
This book has been carefully designed to minimise awkward
page turns and to make playing from it a real pleasure.
Particular care has been given to specifying acid-free, neutral-sized paper
made from pulps which have not been elemental chlorine bleached.
This pulp is from farmed sustainable forests and was
produced with special regard for the environment.
Throughout, the printing and binding have been planned to
ensure a sturdy, attractive publication which should give years of enjoyment.
If your copy fails to meet our high standards,
please inform us and we will gladly replace it.

www.musicsales.com

# THE MILLION SELLERS
# CONTENTS

# THE MILLION SELLERS
# AN EXPLANATION

*The Million Sellers* is the definitive guide to the UK's million-selling singles and is published to mark 60 years of the Official Singles Chart in 2012. It is based on a countdown of the all-time biggest-selling singles in the UK, which has been researched and collated by the Official Charts Company (the agency tasked by the UK music industry with overseeing the archive of charts and market data, from 1952 to date), with crucial assistance from Alan Jones, the UK's pre-eminent chart data researcher, who has been writing about the UK's sales charts for *Music Week* and *Record Mirror* for more than 30 years.

This list has been based on electronic records held by the Official Charts Company dating back to spring 1994, combined with researched data for the period prior to this – including contemporaneously published reports, official record label returns and a wide range of other sources. This is the definitive list of the UK's all-time biggest-selling singles, from 1952 to the end of May 2012 (the cut-off point owing to publishing deadlines).

In practice, the first officially recognised singles chart in the UK was that which was compiled from 1969 by the British Market Research Bureau, supported by the BBC and trade newspaper *Record Retailer*. Before this time, there were a range of charts operating in the UK, compiled by different media outlets. However, the charts which are today widely recognised as being the UK's 'official' charts began with the *New Musical Express*-published charts from November 1952 until 1960, followed by the *Record Retailer* charts published from 1960 until 1969. For this book, we have taken these as the UK's 'Official Charts', even though they were not known by this name at the time.

The data banks accompanying every one of these entries are based on the information commonly accepted to be correct at the time of publication, and do not take into account any disputes which may occur after the end of May 2012. Weeks on chart refers to weeks in the Top 75, as based on the Official Charts Company's own charts history database. All of the information in this databank (including peak chart positions, weeks in this position and weeks on chart) is correct up to this cut-off date (end of May 2012).

WRITERS: Robbie Williams, Guy Chambers
PRODUCERS: Guy Chambers, Steve Power
ALBUM: Life Thru A Lens
PEAK POSITION: Number 4 (1 week)
WEEKS ON CHART: 27
SALES: 1.11m

ROBBIE WILLIAMS 1997

# ANGELS

Words & Music by Robbie Williams & Guy Chambers
© Copyright 1997 Kobalt Music Publishing Limited/EMI Virgin Music Limited.
All Rights Reserved. International Copyright Secured.

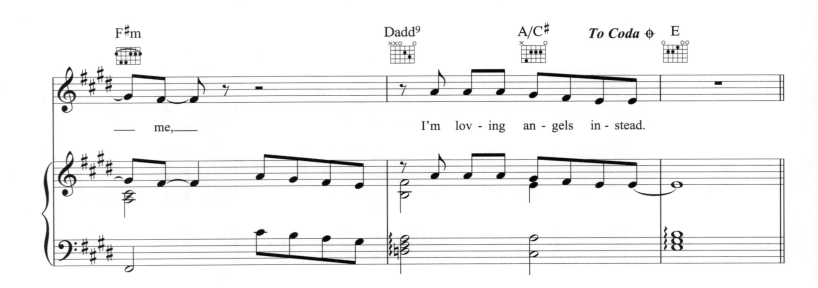

And through it all_____ she of-fers me__ pro-tec - tion,____ a lot of love and af-fec-

WRITER: Max Martin
PRODUCERS: Max Martin, Rami Yacoub, Denniz Pop
ALBUM: ...Baby One More Time
PEAK POSITION: Number 1 (2 weeks)
WEEKS ON CHART: 22
SALES: 1.51m

**BRITNEY SPEARS** 1999

# ...BABY ONE MORE TIME

Words & Music by Max Martin
© Copyright 1998 Imagem London Limited.
All Rights Reserved. International Copyright Secured.

still be - lieve,___ still be - lieve.___ When I'm not with you I lose my mind. Give me a sign,___

hit me ba - by one more time.

hit me ba - by one more time.

WRITER: Gary Barlow
PRODUCERS: Chris Porter, Gary Barlow
ALBUM: Nobody Else
PEAK POSITION: Number 1 (4 weeks)
WEEKS ON CHART: 13
SALES: 1.07m

TAKE THAT 1995

# BACK FOR GOOD

1. I guess___ now it's time___
2. Un-a-ware,___ but un-der-lined___

___ for me to give up, I feel it's time.___ Got a
___ I fig-ured out the sto-ry, it was-n't good.___ But in a

Words & Music by Gary Barlow
© Copyright 1995 EMI Virgin Music Limited.
All Rights Reserved. International Copyright Secured.

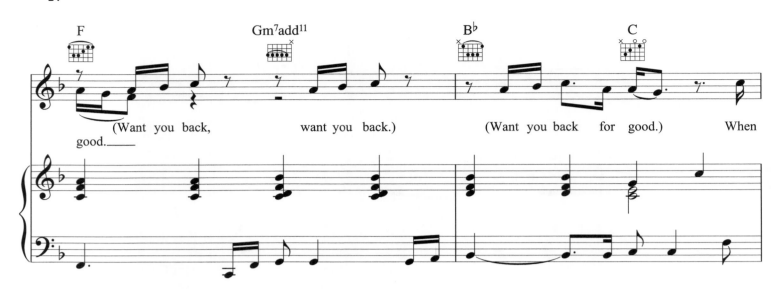

(Want you back, want you back.) (Want you back for good.) When good.____

-ev - er I'm wrong just tell me the song__ and I'll sing__ it._____ You'll be right and__ un - der -

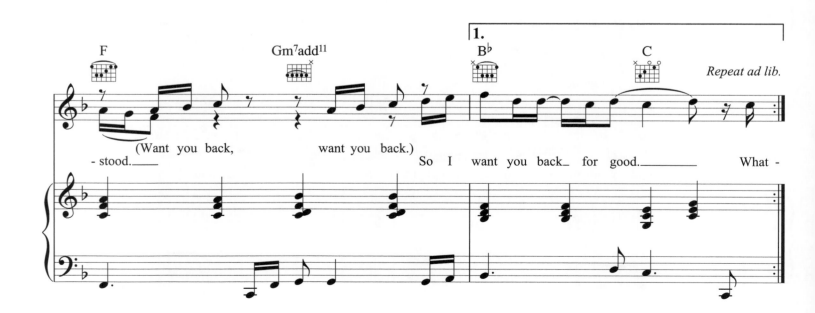

(Want you back, want you back.) - stood.____ So I want you back__ for good._____ What -

*Repeat ad lib.*

want you back__ for good._____ Oh,_____ yeah.__

I guess____ now it's time__

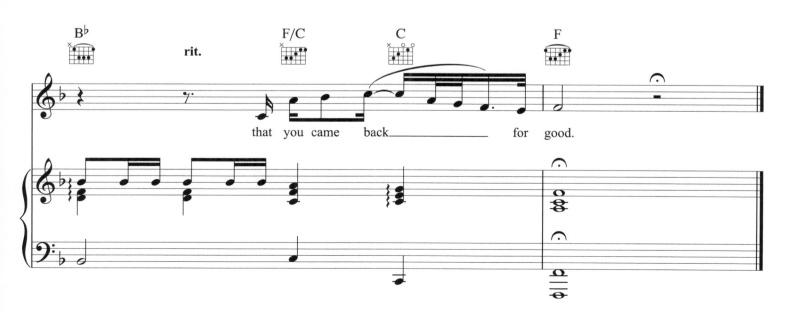

that you came back_____ for good.

**AQUA** 1997

# BARBIE GIRL

WRITERS: Claus Norreen, Søren Nystrøm Rasted

PRODUCERS: Søren Nystrøm Rasted, Claus Norreen, Johnny Jam, Delgado

ALBUM: Aquarium

PEAK POSITION: Number 1 (4 weeks)

WEEKS ON CHART: 26

SALES: 1.79m

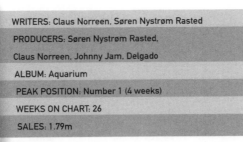

Words & Music by Søren Rasted, Claus Norreen, Rene Dif, Johnny Pederson, Karsten Delgado & Lene Nystrom

© Copyright 1997 Universal/MCA Music Scandinavia AB/Fintage Talent BV.

Warner/Chappell Music Limited/Universal/MCA Music Limited.

All Rights Reserved. International Copyright Secured.

# LEONA LEWIS 2007
# BLEEDING LOVE

WRITERS: Ryan Tedder, Jesse McCartney
PRODUCER: Ryan Tedder
ALBUM: Spirit
PEAK POSITION: Number 1 (7 weeks)
WEEKS ON CHART: 28
SALES: 1.04m

Words & Music by Ryan Tedder & Jesse McCartney
© Copyright 2007 Write 2 Live Publishing/Jambition Music, USA.
Kobalt Music Publishing Limited/Warner/Chappell Artemis Music Limited.
All Rights Reserved. International Copyright Secured.

WRITER: Freddie Mercury

PRODUCERS: Roy Thomas Baker, Freddie Mercury, John Deacon, Brian May, Roger Taylor

ALBUM: A Night At The Opera

PEAK POSITION: Number 1 (9 weeks, 1975)/ Number 1 (5 weeks, 1991)

WEEKS ON CHART: 31 (1975, 17; 1991, 14)

SALES: 2.36m

QUEEN 1975

# BOHEMIAN RHAPSODY

*Con pedale*

Words & Music by Freddie Mercury
© Copyright 1975 Queen Music Limited.
EMI Music Publishing Limited.
All Rights Reserved. International Copyright Secured.

I don't wan-na die,__ I some-times wish I'd nev-er been born at all.__

(An- y-way the wind blows.)

Guitar Solo

eye._____

So__ you think you__ can love me__ and leave me__ to die._____ Oh_____

ba - by,_____ can't_ do this to__ me ba - by._____

Just got-ta get out,__ just got-ta get right out - ta here._____

(Ooh._____

Ooh___ yeah,      ooh___ yeah.)

WRITERS: Elton John. Bernie Taupin

PRODUCER: George Martin

ALBUM: The Big Picture (Something About
The Way You Look Tonight)

PEAK POSITION: Number 1 (5 weeks)

WEEKS ON CHART: 24

SALES: 4.9m

ELTON JOHN 1997

# CANDLE IN THE WIND 1997

**Moderately**

1. Good-bye Eng - land's rose,___ may you ev-er grow in our hearts,___ you were___ the grace that placed it - self___ where lives were torn___ a - part.___ You called out to our

Words & Music by Elton John & Bernie Taupin

© Copyright 1973 Dick James Music Limited.

Universal/Dick James Music Limited.

All Rights Reserved. International Copyright Secured.

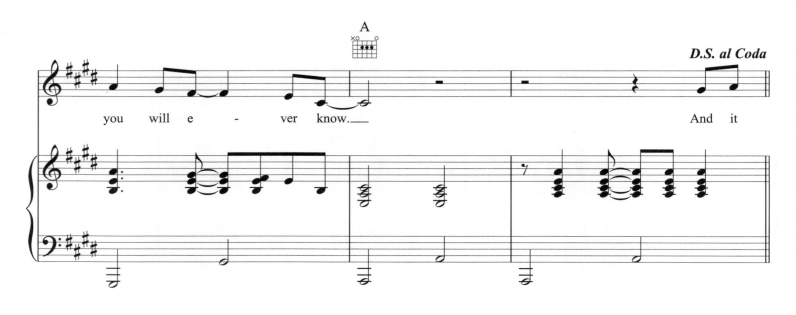

*D.S. al Coda*

you will e - ver know.___ And it

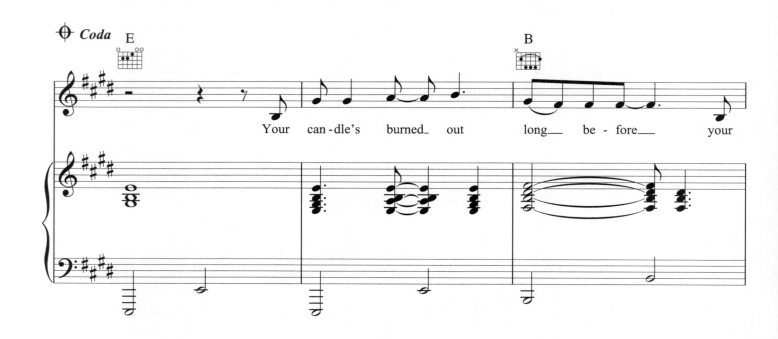

*Coda*

Your can-dle's burned_ out long___ be-fore___ your

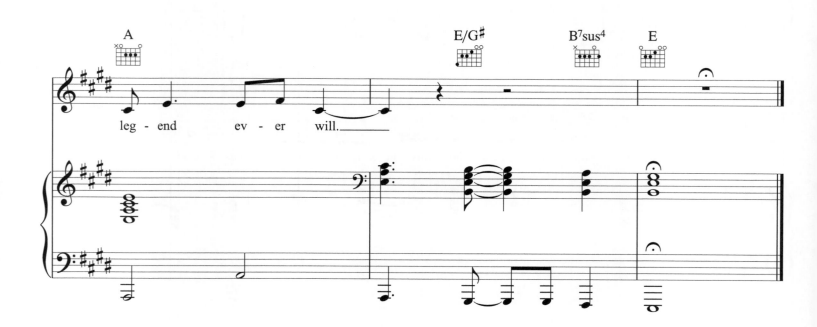

leg - end ev - er will._____

KYLIE MINOGUE 2001
# CAN'T GET YOU OUT OF MY HEAD

| | |
|---|---|
| **WRITERS:** Cathy Dennis, Rob Davis | |
| **PRODUCERS:** Cathy Dennis, Rob Davis | |
| **ALBUM:** Fever | |
| **PEAK POSITION:** Number 1 (4 weeks) | |
| **WEEKS ON CHART:** 25 | |
| **SALES:** 1.15m | |

Words & Music by Cathy Dennis & Rob Davis
© Copyright 2001 EMI Music Publishing Limited/Universal/MCA Music Limited.
All Rights Reserved. International Copyright Secured.

Stay_____ for -

-ev - er_____ and ev - er_____ and ev - er - and ev - er._____

(La la la la_____ la la la la. La la la la_____ la la la la.)

WRITERS: John Lennon, Paul McCartney
PRODUCER: George Martin
ALBUM: A Hard Day's Night
PEAK POSITION: Number 1 (3 weeks)
WEEKS ON CHART: 17 (1964, 15; 1984, 2)
SALES: 1.53m

THE BEATLES 1964

# CAN'T BUY ME LOVE

Can't buy me love,_____ oh,_____ love,__ _____ oh,_____ can't buy me love,_____ oh._____ 1. I'll

buy you a dia-mond ring____ my friend____ if it makes you feel all right,__
(2.) give you all I've got____ to give____ if you say you love me too,__

Words & Music by John Lennon & Paul McCartney
© Copyright 1964 Sony/ATV Music Publishing.
All Rights Reserved. International Copyright Secured.

JULIE COVINGTON 1976

# DON'T CRY FOR ME ARGENTINA

WRITERS: Andrew Lloyd Webber, Tim Rice
PRODUCERS: Andrew Lloyd Webber, Tim Rice
ALBUM: Evita
PEAK POSITION: Number 1 (1 week)
WEEKS ON CHART: 18 (1976, 15: 1978, 3)
SALES: 1.01m

**Slowly** (♩ = 78)

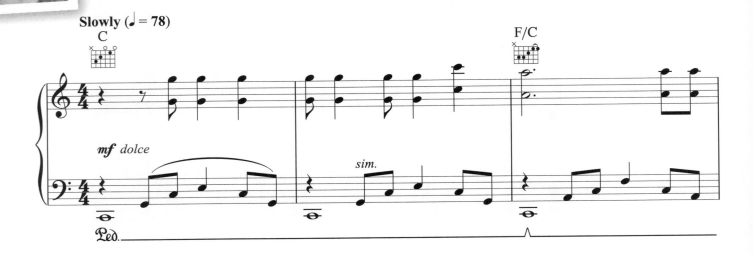

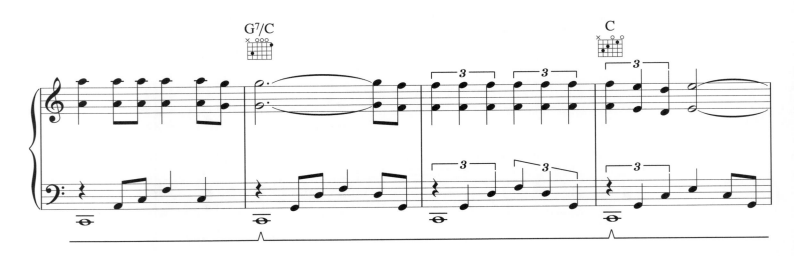

Music by Andrew Lloyd Webber
Lyrics by Tim Rice
© Copyright 1976 & 1977 Evita Music Limited.
All Rights Reserved. International Copyright Secured.

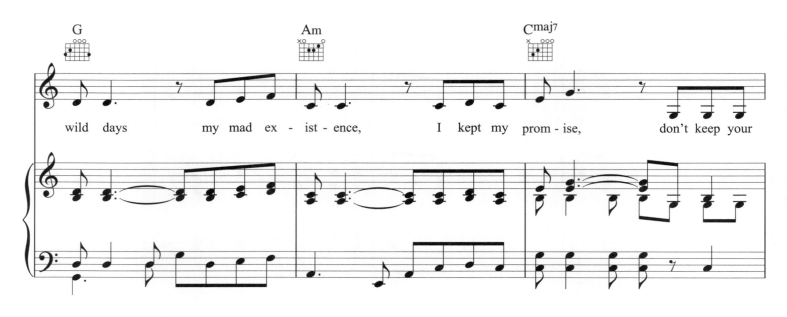

wild days my mad ex - ist - ence, I kept my prom - ise, don't keep your

dis - tance.__ Have I said too much? There's noth - ing more I can think of to

pp colla voce

say to you. But

ppp

all you have to do is look at me to know that ev-'ry word is true.

WRITER: Tony Macaulay
PRODUCER: Tony Macaulay
ALBUM: David Soul
PEAK POSITION: Number 1 (4 weeks)
WEEKS ON CHART: 16
SALES: 1.16m

DAVID SOUL 1976

# DON'T GIVE UP ON US

Words & Music by Tony Macaulay
© Copyright 1976 Macaulay Music Limited.
Universal Music Publishing Limited.
All Rights Reserved. International Copyright Secured.

WRITERS: Philip Oakey, Jo Callis, Philip Adrian Wright

PRODUCER: Martin Rushent

ALBUM: Dare

PEAK POSITION: Number 1 (5 weeks)

WEEKS ON CHART: 13

SALES: 1.54m

**THE HUMAN LEAGUE** 1981

# DON'T YOU WANT ME

Words & Music by Phil Oakey, Jo Callis & Adrian Wright

© Copyright 1981 EMI Virgin Music Limited

V2 Music Publishing Limited.

All Rights Reserved. International Copyright Secured.

Don't you want me ba - by, don't you want me?

Oh._____ Don't you want me ba - by,

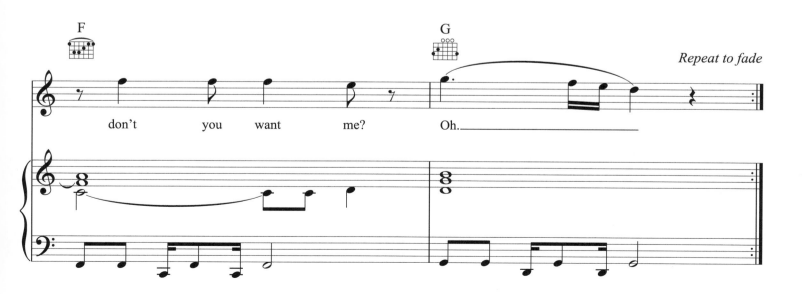

don't you want me? Oh._____

*Repeat to fade*

# DANCING QUEEN

WRITERS: Stig Anderson, Benny Andersson, Björn Ulvaeus

PRODUCERS: Benny Andersson, Björn Ulvaeus

ALBUM: Arrival

PEAK POSITION: Number 1 (6 weeks)

WEEKS ON CHART: 20 (1976, 15; 1992, 5)

SALES: 1.06m

**Strong rock**

You can dance,___ you can jive,___ hav-ing___ the time of___ your

life.___ Ooh,___ see that___ girl,___ watch that___ scene,_ dig-gin' the

Words & Music by Benny Andersson, Stig Anderson & Björn Ulvaeus

© Copyright 1976 Union Songs AB, Sweden.

Bocu Music Limited for Great Britain and the Republic Of Ireland.

All Rights Reserved. International Copyright Secured.

# WILL YOUNG 2002
# EVERGREEN

| WRITERS: Jörgen Elofsson, Per Magnusson, David Kreuger |
| --- |
| PRODUCERS: Per Magnusson, David Kreuger |
| ALBUM: From Now On |
| PEAK POSITION: Number 1 (3 weeks) |
| WEEKS ON CHART: 16 |
| SALES: 1.79m |

Mm.

1. Eyes like a sun-rise, like a rain-fall down my soul.
2. Touch like an an-gel, like vel-vet to my skin.

And I won-der, I won-der why you
And I won-der, I won-der why you

Words & Music by Jörgen Elofsson, Per Magnusson & David Kreuger

© Copyright 2001 Good Ear Music/Decay Music, AB.

Peermusic (UK) Limited/Universal Music Publishing MGB Limited/Warner/Chappell Music Publishing Limited.

All Rights Reserved. International Copyright Secured.

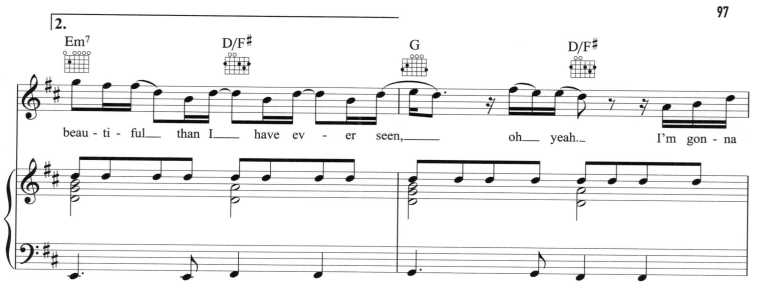

beau - ti - ful__ than I__ have ev - er seen,__ oh__ yeah.__ I'm gon - na

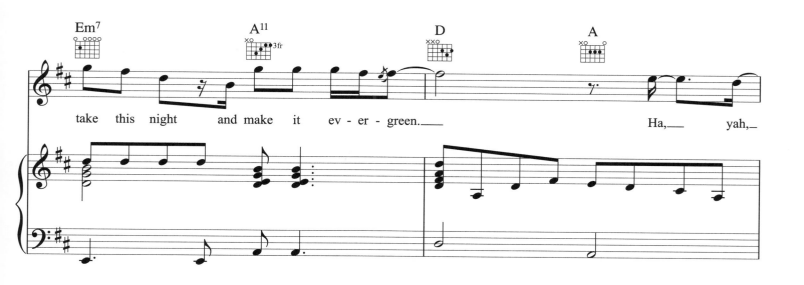

take this night and make it ev - er - green.__ Ha,__ yah,__

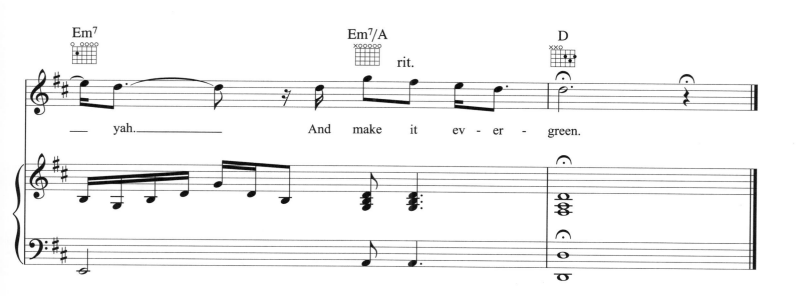

__ yah.__ And make it ev - er - green.

WRITERS: Bryan Adams, Michael Kamen.
Robert John 'Mutt' Lange

PRODUCER: Robert John 'Mutt' Lange

ALBUM: Waking Up The Neighbours/Robin Hood:
Prince Of Thieves (soundtrack)

PEAK POSITION: Number 1 (16 weeks)

WEEKS ON CHART: 25

SALES: 1.72m

BRYAN ADAMS 1991

# (EVERYTHING I DO) I DO IT FOR YOU

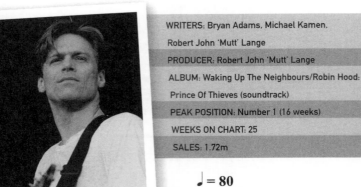

Written by Michael Kamen, Bryan Adams & Robert John Lange

© Copyright 1991 Almo Music Corporation/2855 Music/Out Of Pocket Productions Limited/Zachary Creek Music, Inc. (BMI)/Miracle Creek Music (ASCAP).
Rondor Music (London) Limited/Universal Music Publishing Limited/Fintage Publishing B.V.
All Rights Reserved. International Copyright Secured.

TOM JONES 1966

# GREEN, GREEN GRASS OF HOME

| | |
|---|---|
| WRITER: | Claude 'Curly' Putman, Jr. |
| PRODUCER: | Peter Sullivan |
| ALBUM: | Green, Green Grass Of Home |
| PEAK POSITION: | Number 1 (7 weeks) |
| WEEKS ON CHART: | 22 |
| SALES: | 1.23m |

Words & Music by Curly Putman
© Copyright 1965 Tree Publishing Company Incorporated, USA.
Burlington Music Company Limited.
All Rights Reserved. International Copyright Secured.

Coda

Yes, they'll all come to see me in the shade of that old oak tree, as they lay me 'neath the green, green grass of home.

*Verse 3 (spoken):*
Then I awake and look around me,
At four grey walls that surround me,
And I realise, yes, I was only dreaming.
For there's a guard and there's a sad old padre;
On and on we'll walk at daybreak.
Again I'll touch the green, green grass of home.

BLONDIE 1979
# HEART OF GLASS

WRITERS: Deborah Harry, Chris Stein

PRODUCER: Mike Chapman

ALBUM: Parallel Lines

PEAK POSITION: Number 1 (4 weeks)

WEEKS ON CHART: 12

SALES: 1.27m

1. Once I had a love_____ and it__ was a gas,__

Words & Music by Deborah Harry & Chris Stein
© Copyright 1978 Rare Blue Music Incorporated/Monster Island Music Incorporated, USA.
Chrysalis Music Limited.
All Rights Reserved. International Copyright Secured.

just no good, you teas-ing like you do.____

just no good, you teas-ing like you do.____

ALEXADRA BURKE 2008

# HALLELUJAH

WRITER: Leonard Cohen

PRODUCERS: Andreas Romdhane, Josef Larossi

ALBUM: Overcome

PEAK POSITION: Number 1 (3 weeks)

WEEKS ON CHART: 12 (2008, 11; 2009, 1)

SALES: 1.24m

1. I

heard there was a se-cret chord that Dav-id played, and it pleased the Lord,

(2.) faith was strong but you need-ed proof, you saw her bath-ing on the roof,_ her

but you don't_ real-ly care for mu-sic, do ya?_____ Well, it

beau-ty_____ and the moon-light_ o-ver threw ya._____ She

Words & Music by Leonard Cohen
© Copyright 1984 Sony/ATV Music Publishing.
All Rights Reserved. International Copyright Secured.

STEVIE WONDER 1984

# I JUST CALLED TO SAY I LOVE YOU

| WRITER: Stevie Wonder |
| PRODUCER: Stevie Wonder |
| ALBUM: The Woman In Red (soundtrack) |
| PEAK POSITION: Number 1 (6 weeks) |
| WEEKS ON CHART: 26 |
| SALES: 1.83m |

Lyrics (beneath staves):

1. No New Year's Day to cel - e - brate; no choc - 'late cov - ered can - dy hearts

(2.) rain; no flow - ers bloom; no wed - ding Sat - ur - day with - in

*(Verses 3&4, see additional lyrics)*

Words & Music by Stevie Wonder

© Copyright 1984 Jobete Music Company Incorporated/Black Bull Music Incorporated, USA.

Jobete Music (UK) Limited.

All Rights Reserved. International Copyright Secured.

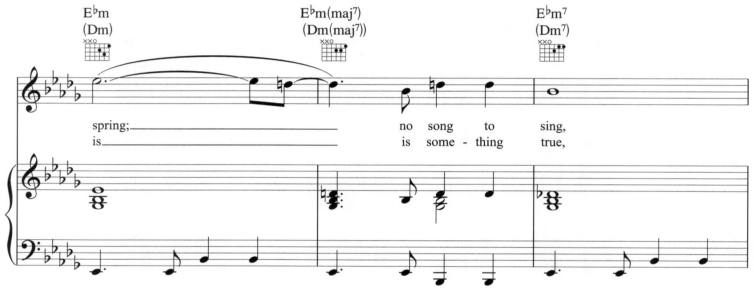

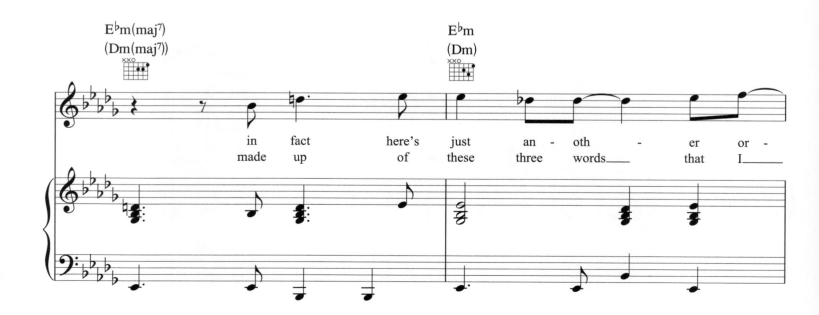

*Additional lyrics*

(Verse 3)
No summer's high, no warm July;
No harvest moon to light one tender August night.
No autumn breeze, no falling leaves;
Not even time for birds to fly to southern skies.

(Verse 4)
No Libra sun, no Halloween;
No giving thanks to all the Christmas joy you bring.
But what it is, though old so new
To fill your heart like no three words could ever do.
*(To Chorus)*

WRITER: Dolly Parton

PRODUCER: David Foster

ALBUM: The Bodyguard: Original Soundtrack

PEAK POSITION: Number 1 (10 weeks)

WEEKS ON CHART: 31 (1992: 23; 1993: 6; 2012: 2)

SALES: 1.53m

**WHITNEY HOUSTON** 1992

# I WILL ALWAYS LOVE YOU

Words & Music by Dolly Parton

© Copyright 1973 Velvet Apple Music, USA.

Carlin Music Corporation for the world

(excluding Germany, Austria, Switzerland, Scandinavia, Eastern Europe, Australia, New Zealand, Japan, South Africa, Canada and the United States of America).

All Rights Reserved. International Copyright Secured.

will al-ways love_ you,_____ I_____

will_ al - ways love_ you._____

*(1° saxophone solo)*

(2.) hope         life___ treats you___ kind,___     and I___ hope_____ you have all you    dreamed

of._____ And I wish you joy__ and__hap-pi - ness:_____ but, a-bove all__

— this, I__ wish you_____ I__ love._____

And I_____ will al - ways_ love_

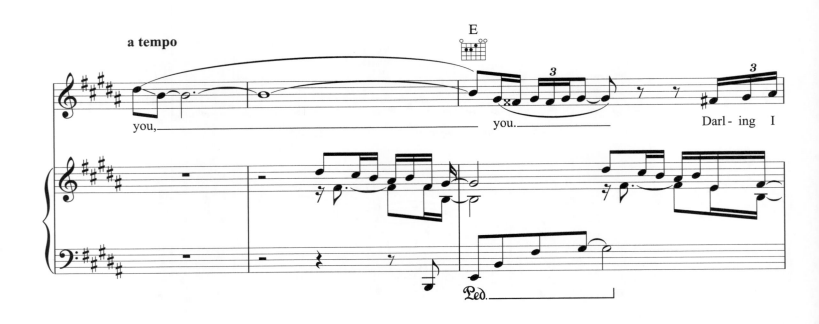

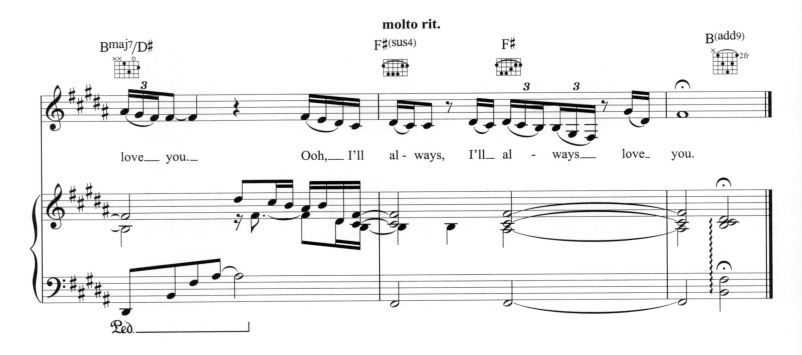

# JOHN LENNON 1975
# IMAGINE

WRITER: John Lennon

PRODUCERS: John Lennon, Yoko Ono, Phil Spector

ALBUM: Imagine

PEAK POSITION: Number 6 (1975)

Number 1 (4 weeks, 1980)

WEEKS ON CHART: 43 (1975, 11; 1980, 13; 1988, 5; 1999, 14)

SALES: 1.6m

♩ = 76

*pp ad lib. throughout

1. I-ma-gine there's no heav-en,        it's eas-y    if you try._____

No hell___ be-low us,_____        a-bove us on-ly  sky.

Words & Music by John Lennon

© Copyright 1971 Lenono Music.

All Rights Reserved. International Copyright Secured.

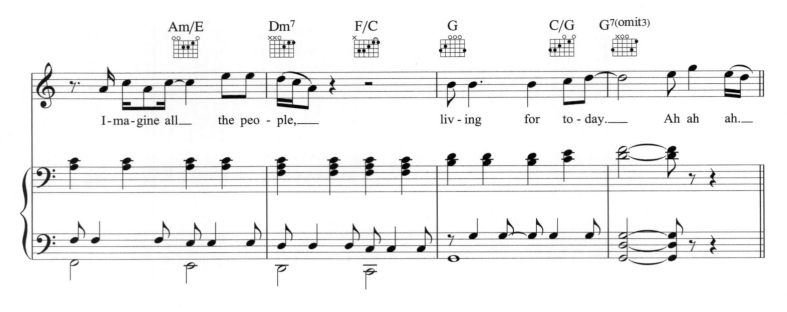

I-ma-gine all___ the peo - ple,___ liv - ing for to - day.___ Ah ah ah.___

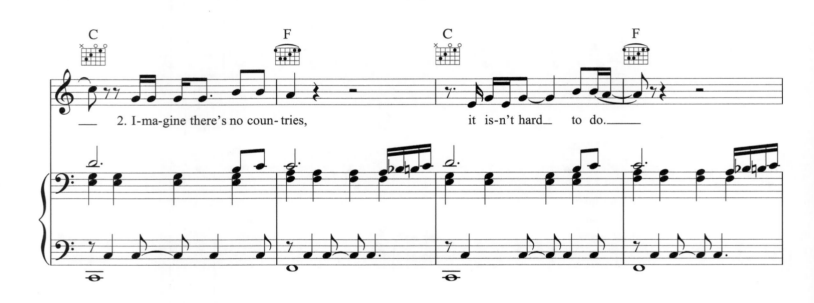

2. I-ma-gine there's no coun- tries, it is-n't hard___ to do.___

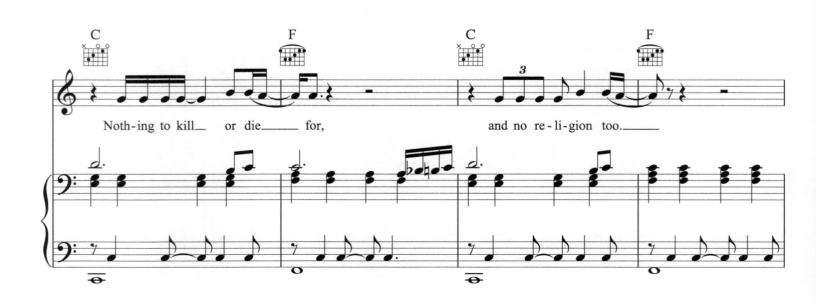

Noth-ing to kill___ or die___ for, and no re-li-gion too.___

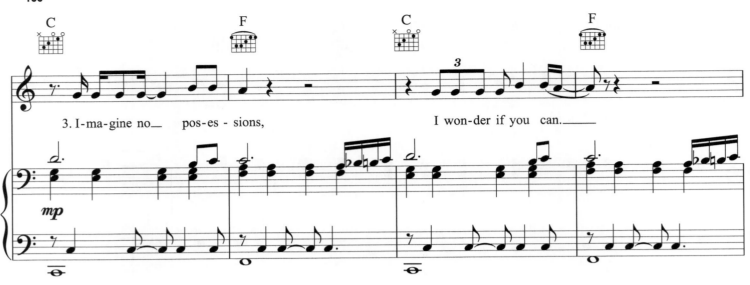

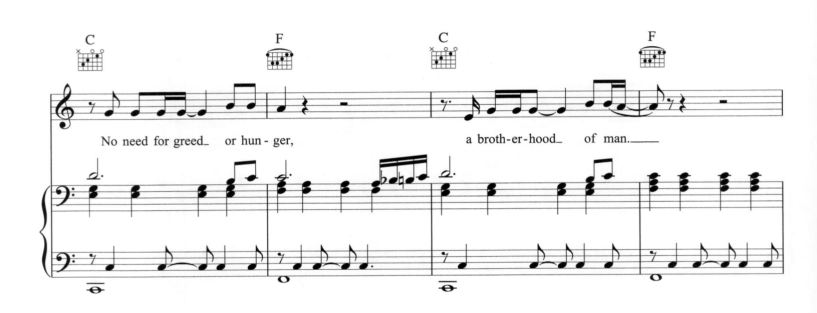

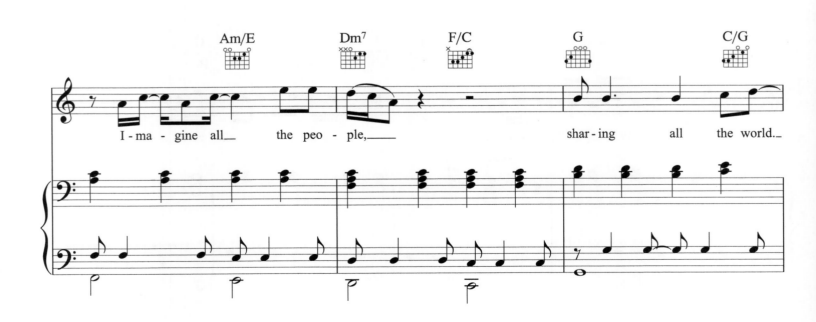

You,_____ you may say_____ I'm a dream-er,

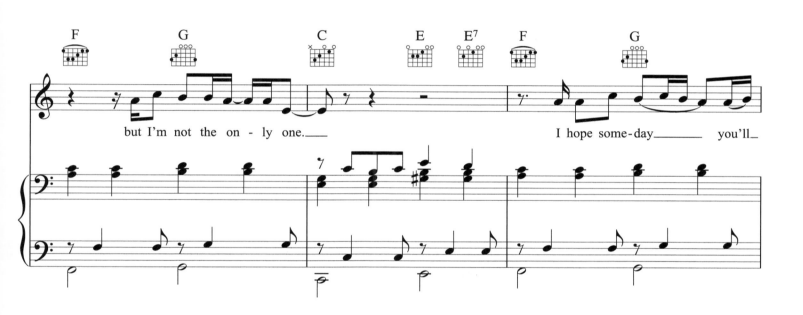

but I'm not the on - ly one.____ I hope some-day_____ you'll_

join us,_____ and the world_____ will live as one.____

WRITERS: Eduardo di Capua (melody).
Aaron Schroeder (lyrics). Wally Gold (lyrics)
PRODUCERS: Steve Sholes. Chet Akins
ALBUM: N/A
PEAK POSITION: Number 1 (8 weeks)
WEEKS ON CHART: 25 (1960. 19: 1977. 2: 2005. 4)
SALES: 1.26m

ELVIS PRESLEY 1960

# IT'S NOW OR NEVER

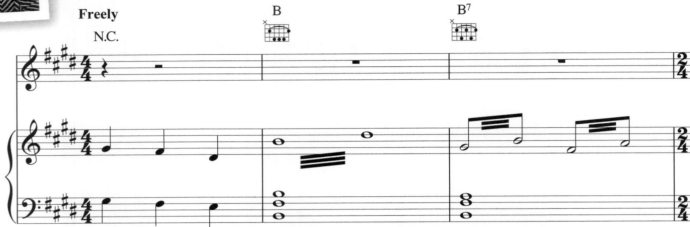

Words & Music by Wally Gold, Aaron Schroeder & Eduardo Di Capua
© Copyright 1960 Rachel's Own Music, USA.
Minder Music Limited.
All Rights Reserved. International Copyright Secured.

140

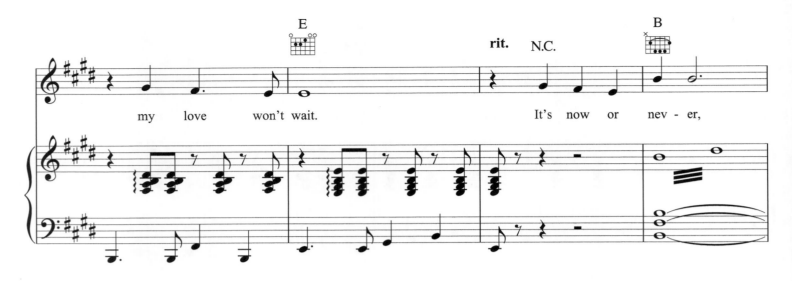

my love won't wait. It's now or nev - er,

my love won't wait. It's now or nev - er,

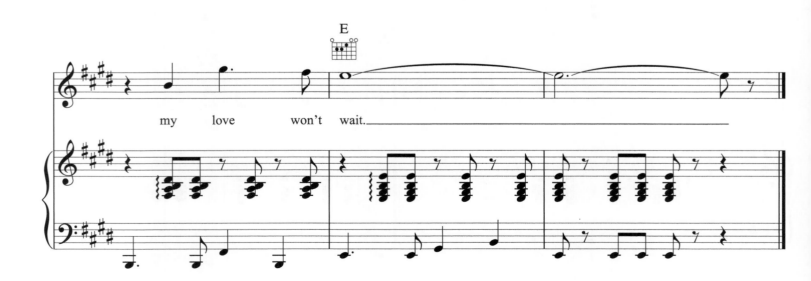

my love won't wait._____

WET WET WET 1994
# LOVE IS ALL AROUND

WRITER: Reg Presley

PRODUCERS: Graeme Clark, Graeme Duffin, Marti Pellow, Tommy Cunningham, Neil Mitchell

ALBUM: Picture This/Four Weddings And A Funeral (soundtrack)

PEAK POSITION: Number 1 (15 weeks)

WEEKS ON CHART: 37

SALES: 1.85m

1. I feel it in my fin - gers, I feel it in my toes._
(2.) see your face be - fore me as I lay on my bed._

The love that's all a - round me
I can - not get to think - ing

Words & Music by Reg Presley
© Copyright 1967 Dick James Music Limited.
Universal/Dick James Music Limited.
All Rights Reserved. International Copyright Secured.

2. I — Got to keep it mov-ing. It's

writ - ten in the wind oh, ev -'ry-where I go.

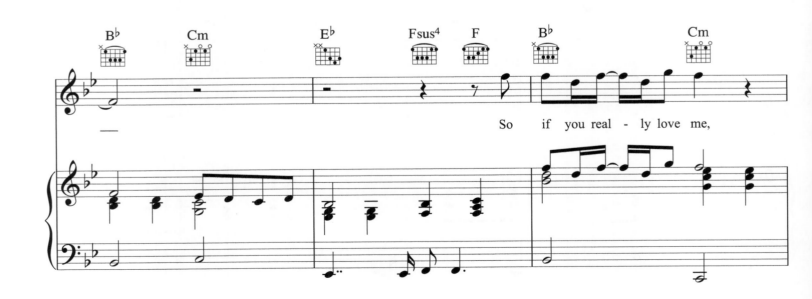

So if you real - ly love me,

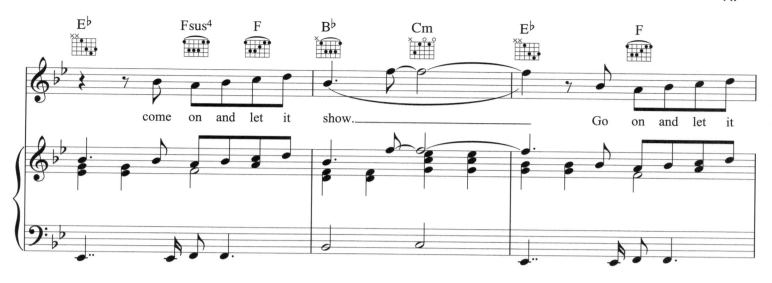

come on and let it show._____ Go on and let it

Go on and let_____ it, come on and let_____ it,
(show.)

*Repeat and fade*

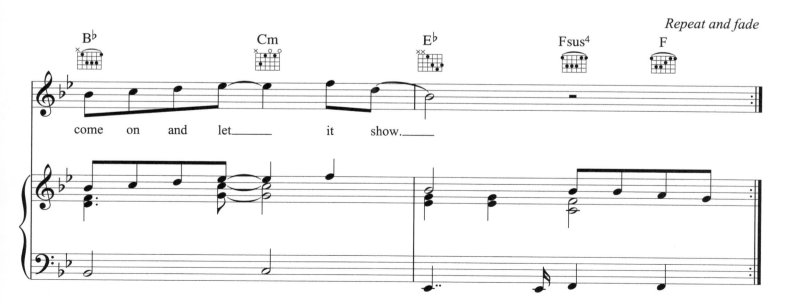

come on and let_____ it show._____

WRITERS: Marshall Mathers III (lyrics),
Alexander Grant, Holly Hafermann
PRODUCERS: Alex da Kid, Makeba Riddick
ALBUM: Recovery
PEAK POSITION: Number 2 (4 weeks)
WEEKS ON CHART: 44
SALES: 1.05m

EMINEM FEAT. RIHANNA 2010

# LOVE THE WAY YOU LIE

Words & Music by Marshall Mathers, Alexander Grant & H. Hafferman
© Copyright 2010 Songs Of Universal Incorporated/Hotel Bravo Music/Shroom Shady Music, USA.
Universal/MCA Music Limited/Imagem Music Limited.
All Rights Reserved. International Copyright Secured.

lie.

*Verse 2:*
You ever love somebody so much you can barely breathe?
When you with 'em you meet and neither one of you even know what hit 'em.
Got that warm fuzzy feeling
Yeah, them those chills used to get 'em
Now you're getting fuckin' sick of lookin' at him.
You swore you'd never hit 'em, never do nothin' to hurt him
Now you're in each other's face spewin' venom in your words when you spit 'em.
You push pull each other's hair,
Scratch claw hit him throw him down pin him,
So lost in the moments when you're in 'em.
It's the rage that took over, it controls you both
So they say you're the best to go your separate ways.
Guess if they don't know you 'cause today that was yesterday,
Yesterday is over, it's a different day.
Sound like broken records playing over but you promised her
Next time you show restraint, you don't get another chance.
Life is no Nintendo game but you lied again
Now you get to watch her leave out the window,
I guess that's why they call it window pane.

*Verse 3:*
Now I know we said things, hit things that we didn't mean
And we fall back into the same patterns same routine.
But your temper's just as bad as mine is,
You're the same as me.
But when it comes to love you're just as blinded.
Baby, please come back it wasn't you, baby it was me,
Maybe our relationship isn't as crazy as it seems.
Maybe that's what happens when a tornado meets a volcano,
All I know is I love you too much to walk away though.
Come inside, pick up your bags off the sidewalk,
Don't you hear sincerity in my voice when I talk?
I told you this is my fault,
Look me in the eyeball
Next time I'm pissed, I'll aim my fist at the drywall.
Next time. There won't be no next time,
I apologize even though I know its lies.
I'm tired of the games I just want her back.
I know I'm a liar,
If she ever tries to fucking leave again
I'm-a tie her to the bed and set this house on fire.

SLADE 1973

# MERRY XMAS EVERYBODY

| WRITERS: Noddy Holder, Jim Lea |
|---|
| PRODUCER: Chas Chandler |
| ALBUM: N/A |
| PEAK POSITION: Number 1 (5 weeks) |
| WEEKS ON CHART: 59 (1973, 9; 1980, 2; 1981, 4; 1982, 3; 1983, 5; 1984, 4; 1985, 3; 1986, 1; 1998, 3; 2006, 5; 2007, 4; 2008, 4; 2009, 4; 2010, 4; 2011, 4) |
| SALES FIGURES: 1.19m |

1. Are you hang-ing up___ a stock-ing on___ your wall?___

*(Verses 2 & 3 see block lyrics)*

It's the time___ that ev-'ry San-ta has___ a ball.___

Words & Music by Neville Holder & James Lea
© Copyright 1973 Barn Publishing (Slade) Limited.
All Rights Reserved. International Copyright Secured.

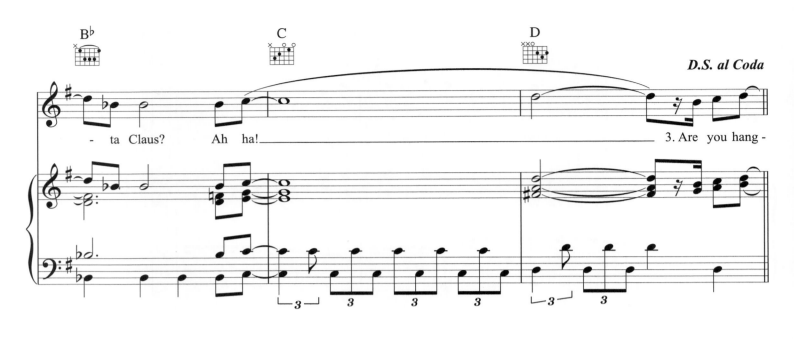

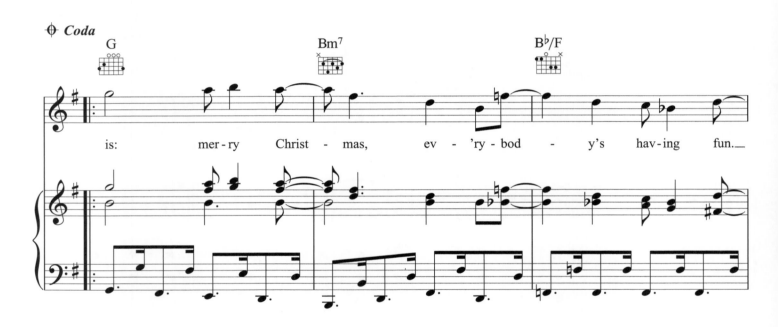

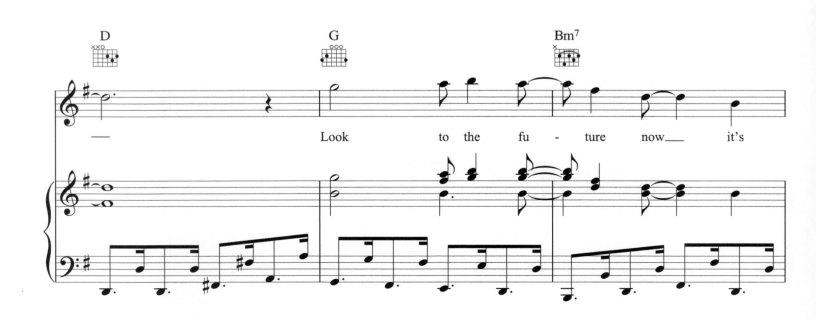

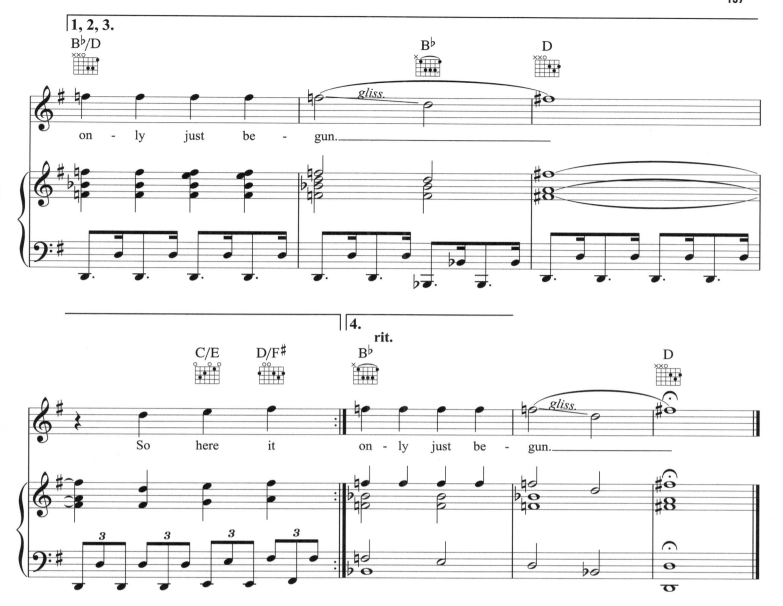

*Verse 2:*
Are you waiting for the family to arrive?
Are you sure you got the room to spare inside?
Does your granny always tell you, that the old songs are the best?
Then she's up and rock 'n' rolling with the best!

*Verse 3:*
Are you hanging up a stocking on your wall?
Are you hoping that the snow will start to fall?
Do you ride on down the hillside in a buggy you have made?
When you land upon your head, then you bin slayed!

WRITERS: 'Mull Of Kintyre' – Paul McCartney, Denny Laine

PRODUCER: Paul McCartney

ALBUM: London Town

PEAK POSITION: Number 1 (9 weeks)

WEEKS ON CHART: 17

SALES: 2m

WINGS 1977

# MULL OF KINTYRE

**Moderately slow**

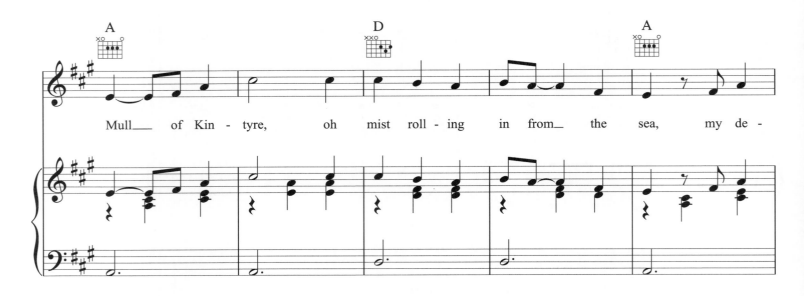

Mull___ of Kin - tyre, oh mist roll - ing in from___ the sea, my de-

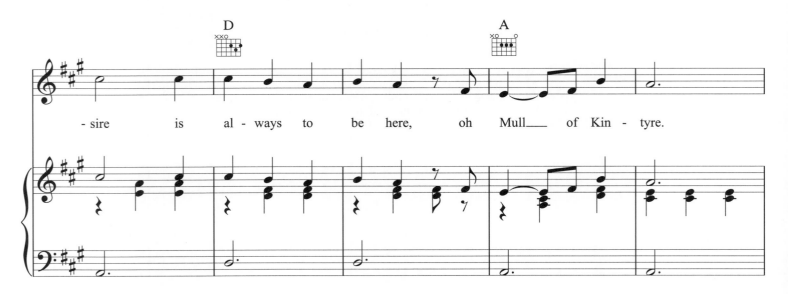

-sire is al - ways to be here, oh Mull___ of Kin - tyre.

Words & Music by Paul McCartney & Denny Laine

© Copyright 1977 MPL Communications Limited.

All Rights Reserved. International Copyright Secured.

Mull___ of Kin - tyre.

Sweep through_ the heath-er___ like deer in the

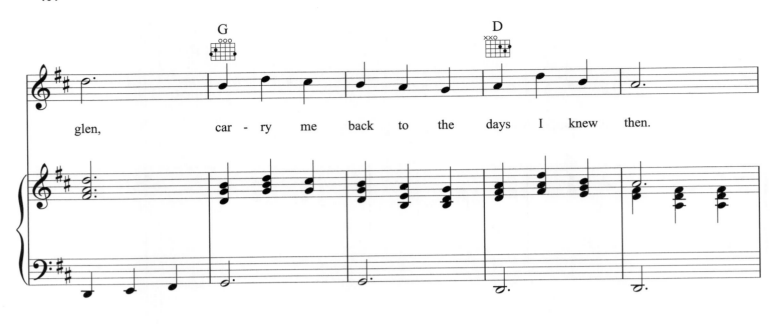

glen, car - ry me back to the days I knew then.

Nights when we sang like a heav - en - ly choir of the life and the

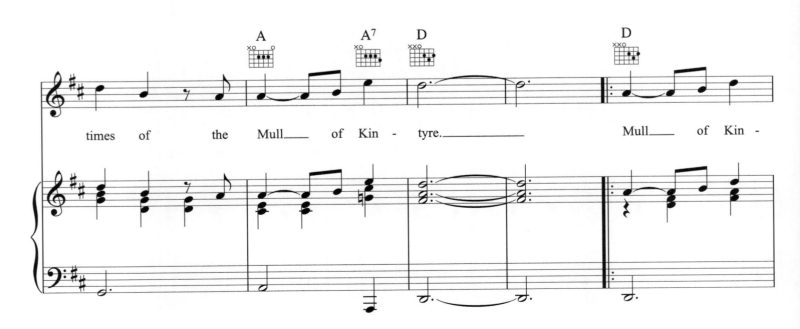

times of the Mull___ of Kin - tyre._____ Mull___ of Kin -

-tyre, oh mist roll - ing in from the sea, my de - sire is

al - ways to be here, oh Mull of Kin - tyre.

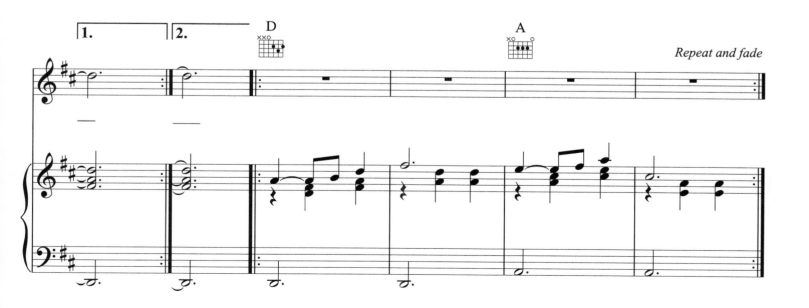

WRITERS: James Horner (music),
Will Jennings (lyrics)
PRODUCERS: Simon Franglen, James Horner,
Walter Afanasieff
ALBUM: Let's Talk About Love/Titanic: Music
From The Motion Picture
PEAK POSITION: Number 1 (2 weeks)
WEEKS ON CHART: 20
SALES: 1.48m

CELINE DION 1998

# MY HEART WILL GO ON

1. Ev - 'ry night in my dreams I see you, I
2. Love can touch us one time and last for a

*Con pedale*

Words by Will Jennings
Music by James Horner
© Copyright 1997 Blue Sky Rider Songs/Fox Film Music Corporation/TCF Music Publishing Inc.
Universal Music Publishing Limited/EMI Music Publishing Limited.
All Rights Reserved. International Copyright Secured.

MAROON 5 FEAT. CHRISTINA AGUILERA 2011

# MOVES LIKE JAGGER

WRITERS: Adam Levine, Benny Blanco (Benjamin Levin), Ammar Malik, Shellback (Karl Schuster)

PRODUCERS: Shellback, Benny Blanco

ALBUM: Hands All Over

PEAK POSITION: Number 2 (7 weeks)

WEEKS ON CHART: 42

SALES: 1.27m

1. Just shoot for the stars,___

Words & Music by Adam Levine, Benjamin Levin, Shellback & Ammar Malik

© Copyright 2011 Universal Music Careers/Matza Ball Music/Where Da Kasz At/Sudgee Music/Maru Cha Cha/MXM Music AB, Sweden.
Kobalt Music Publishing Limited/Universal Music Publishing MGB Limited.
All Rights Reserved. International Copyright Secured.

BOYZONE 1998

# NO MATTER WHAT

| WRITERS: Andrew Lloyd Webber (music), Jim Steinman (lyrics) |
| PRODUCERS: Jim Steinman, Andrew Lloyd Webber, Nigel Wright |
| ALBUM: Where We Belong |
| PEAK POSITION: Number 1 (3 weeks) |
| WEEKS ON CHART: 15 |
| SALES: 1.13m |

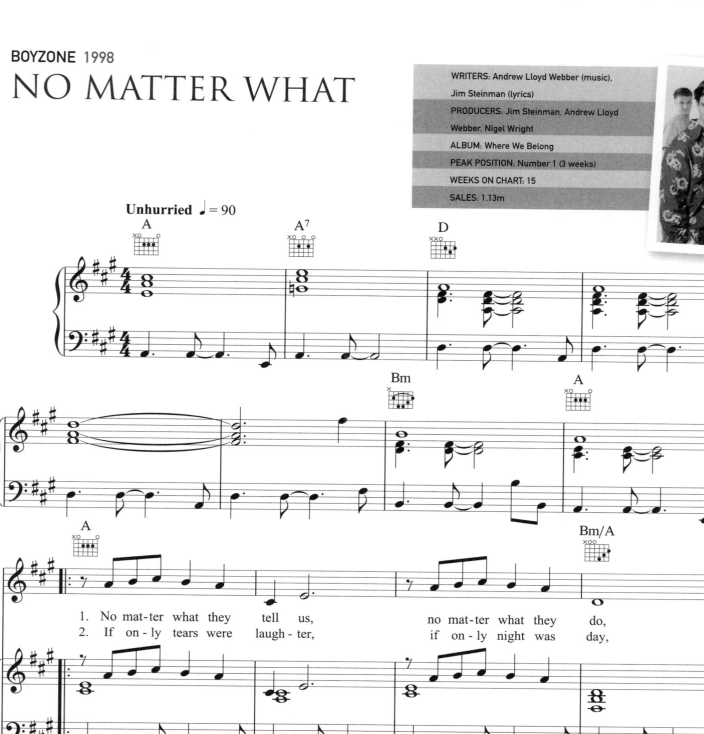

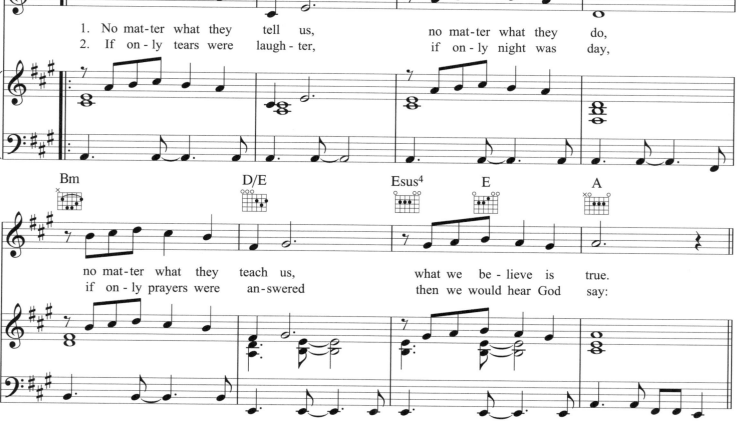

1. No mat-ter what they tell us, no mat-ter what they do,
2. If on-ly tears were laugh-ter, if on-ly night was day,

no mat-ter what they teach us, what we be-lieve is true.
if on-ly prayers were an-swered then we would hear God say:

Music by Andrew Lloyd Webber
Lyrics by Jim Steinman
© Copyright 1998 Andrew Lloyd Webber licensed to The Really Useful Group Limited/Lost Boys Music/Universal Music Publishing Limited.
All Rights Reserved. International Copyright Secured.

I know our love's for-ev-er,
No mat-ter where it's bar-ren

I know no mat-ter what..
our dream is be-ing born..

Instrumental

# NEVER EVER

WRITERS: Rickidy Raw (Robert 'Esmail' Jazayeri, Sean 'Mystro' Mather), Shaznay Lewis

PRODUCERS: Cameron McVey. Magnus Fiennes. Rickidy Raw

ALBUM: All Saints

PEAK POSITION: Number 1 (1 week)

WEEKS ON CHART: 24

SALES: 1.31m

(Spoken) A few questions that I need to know, how you could ever hurt me so? I need to know what I've done wrong,

and how long it's been going on. Was it that I never paid enough attention,

or did I not give enough affection? Not only will your answers keep me sane,

but I'll know never to make the same mistake again. You can tell me to my face

Words & Music by Shaznay Lewis, Esmail Jazayeri & Sean Mather
© Copyright 1997 Rickidy Raw Productions Inc.
Universal/MCA Music Limited/Universal Music Publishing MGB Limited.
All Rights Reserved. International Copyright Secured.

LADY GAGA 2009

# POKER FACE

WRITERS: Stefani Germanotta, Nadir Khayat
PRODUCER: RedOne (Nadir Khayat)
ALBUM: The Fame
PEAK POSITION: Number 1 (3 weeks)
WEEKS ON CHART: 66
SALES: 1.11m

1. I wan-na hold 'em like they do in Tex-as plays:
2. I wan-na roll with him, a hard pair we will be.

Words & Music by Stefani Germanotta & Nadir Khayat
© Copyright 2008 House Of Gaga Publishing Incorporated/Songs Of RedOne/Sony/ATV Songs LLC.
Sony/ATV Music Publishing.
All Rights Reserved. International Copyright Secured.

# PURE AND SIMPLE

WRITERS: Peter Kirtley, Tim Hawes, Alison Clarkson

PRODUCERS: Jiant (Peter Kirtley, Tim Hawes)

ALBUM: Popstars

PEAK POSITION: Number 1 (3 weeks)

WEEKS ON CHART: 25

SALES: 1.09m

1. You been say-ing I'm driv-ing you cra-zy
2. I'll be there through the storm-i-est weath-er,

and I have-n't been a-round for you late-ly,
al-ways try-ing to make things a bit bet-ter

but I had a few things on my mind.
and I know I got-ta try and get through to you.

When I'm with you I am filled with e-mo-tion,
You can love me a way like no oth-er,

can't you see that I'm giv-ing you de-vo-tion,
but the sit-u-a-tion's tak-ing you un-der,

Words & Music by Tim Hawes, Pete Kirtley & Alison Clarkson

© Copyright 2000 Universal Music Publishing Limited/Stage Three Music Publishing Limited/Strongsongs Ltd.

All Rights Reserved. International Copyright Secured.

# RELEASE ME

ENGELBERT HUMPERDINCK 1967

WRITERS: Eddie Miller, James Pebworth, Robert Yount
PRODUCER: Charles Blackwell
ALBUM: Release Me
PEAK POSITION: Number 1 (6 weeks)
WEEKS ON CHART: 57 (1967, 56; 2004, 1)
SALES: 1.38m

Words & Music by Eddie Miller, Dub Williams & Robert Yount
© Copyright 1954 Sony/ATV Acuff Rose Music.
Sony/ATV Music Publishing.
All Rights Reserved. International Copyright Secured.

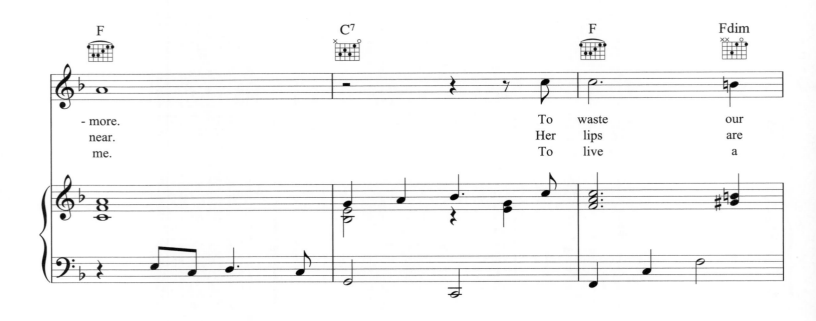

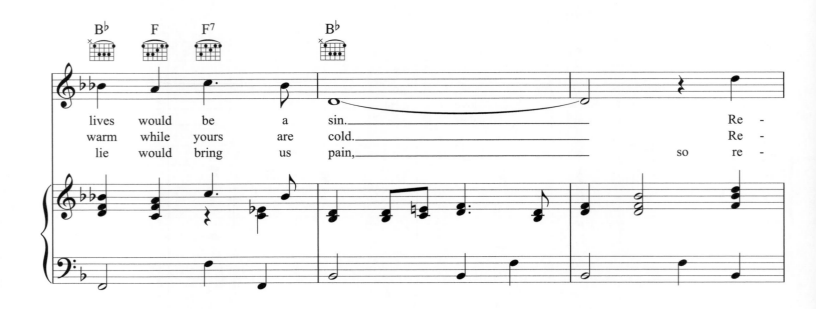

# RELAX

WRITERS: Peter Gill, Holly Johnson, Mark O'Toole

PRODUCER: Trevor Horn

ALBUM: Welcome To The Pleasuredome

PEAK POSITION: Number 1 (5 weeks)

WEEKS ON CHART: 59 (1983, 52; 1993, 7)

SALES: 2m

Words & Music by Peter Gill, Holly Johnson & Mark O'Toole

© Copyright 1984 Perfect Songs Limited.

All Rights Reserved. International Copyright Secured.

WRITERS: Max C. Freedman, James E. Myers

PRODUCER: Milt Gabler

ALBUM: Rock Around The Clock

PEAK POSITION: Number 1 (5 weeks)

WEEKS ON CHART: 57

(1955, 19; 1956, 17; 1968, 11; 1974, 10)

SALES: 1.42m

BILL HALEY & HIS COMETS 1955

# ROCK AROUND THE CLOCK

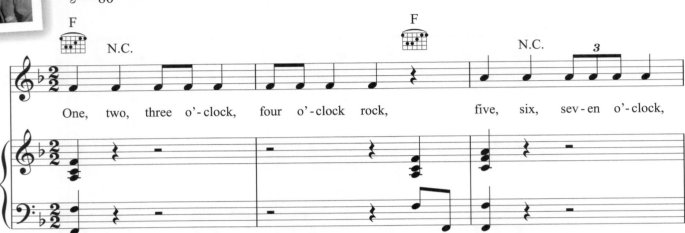

Words & Music by Max C. Freedman & Jimmy De Knight

© Copyright 1953 Myers Music Incorporated, USA.

Edward Kassner Music Company Limited.

All Rights Reserved. International Copyright Secured.

glad rags on and join me, hon,___ we'll have some fun when the

*(Verse 2 -5 see block lyric)*

clock strikes one,___ we're gon - na rock a - round the clock to - night,___ we're gon - na

rock, rock, rock, till broad day - light,___ we're gon - na rock, gon - na rock a - round___

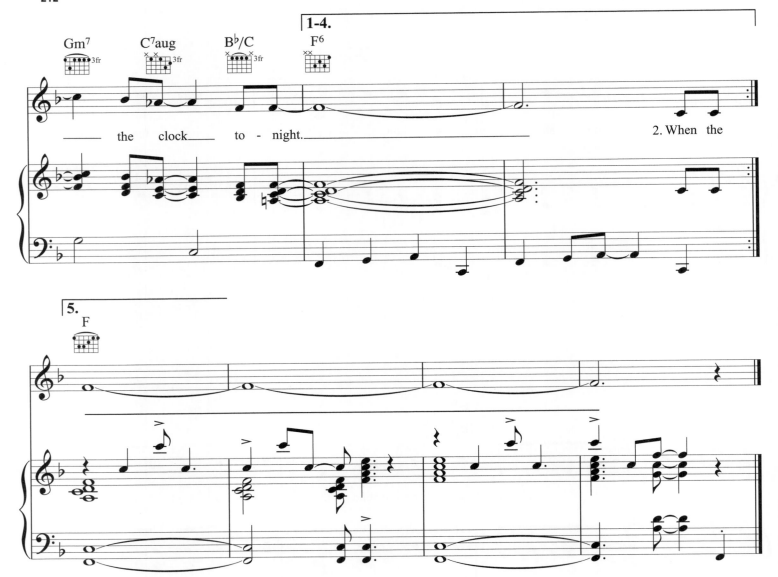

*Verse 2:*
When the clock strikes two and three and four
If the band slows down we'll yell for more.
We're gonna rock around the clock tonight
We're gonna rock, rock, rock till broad daylight
We're gonna rock, gonna rock around the clock tonight.

*Verse 3:*
When the chimes ring five and six and seven
We'll be rockin' up in seventh heav'n.
We're gonna rock around the clock tonight
We're gonna rock, rock, rock till broad daylight
We're gonna rock, gonna rock around the clock tonight.

*Verse 4:*
When it's eight, nine, ten, eleven, too
I'll be goin' strong and so will you.
We're gonna rock around the clock tonight
We're gonna rock, rock, rock till broad daylight
We're gonna rock, gonna rock around the clock tonight.

*Verse 5:*
When the clock strikes twelve, we'll cool off, then
Start a rockin' 'round the clock again.
We're gonna rock around the clock tonight
We're gonna rock, rock, rock till broad daylight
We're gonna rock, gonna rock around the clock tonight.

ROD STEWART 1975
# SAILING

| | |
|---|---|
| WRITER: | Gavin Sutherland |
| PRODUCER: | Tom Dowd |
| ALBUM: | Atlantic Crossing |
| PEAK POSITION: | Number 1 (4 weeks) |
| WEEKS ON CHART: | 34 (1975, 11; 1976, 20; 1987, 3) |
| SALES: | 1.02m |

Words & Music by Gavin Sutherland
© Copyright 1972 Island Music Limited.
Universal/Island Music Limited.
All Rights Reserved. International Copyright Secured.

# SEX ON FIRE

**WRITERS:** Nathan Followill, Caleb Followill, Matthew Followill, Jared Followill

**PRODUCERS:** Angelo Petraglia, Jacquire King

**ALBUM:** Only By The Night

**PEAK POSITION:** Number 1 (3 weeks)

**WEEKS ON CHART:** 90 (2008/9, 87; 2012, 3)

**SALES:** 1.2m

1. Lay where you're lay -

Words & Music by Caleb Followill, Nathan Followill, Jared Followill & Matthew Followill
© Copyright 2008 Martha Street Music/Followill Music/Songs Of Combustion Music/McFearless Music/
Coffee Tea Or Me Publishing/Southside Independent Music Publishing/Bug Music-Music Of Windswept.
Warner/Chappell Music North America Limited/Bug Music (Windswept Account)/Bug Music Ltd.
All Rights Reserved. International Copyright Secured.

the kid - die like play,_____
the knuck - les are pale,_____
if it's just to - night,_____

it has peo - ple talk -
feels like you're dy -
oh, it's still the great -

C#m

- ing,        they're talk - ing.
- ing,        you're dy - ing.
- est,        the great - est,        the great - est.

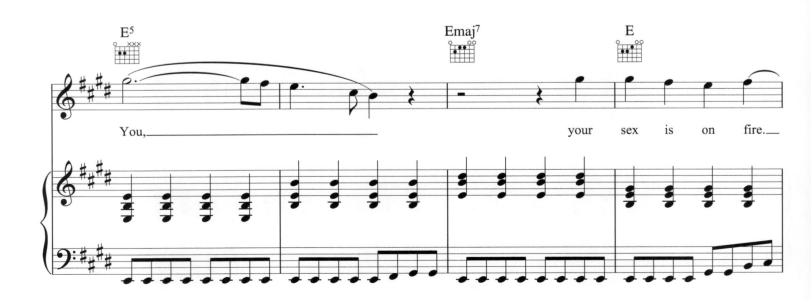

E5        Emaj7        E

You,_____        your sex is on fire._____

WRITERS: John Lennon, Paul McCartney

PRODUCER: George Martin

ALBUM: The Beatles' Second Album

(US-only release)

PEAK POSITION: Number 1 (6 weeks)

WEEKS ON CHART: 36 (1963, 33; 1983, 3)

SALES: 1.9m

THE BEATLES 1963

# SHE LOVES YOU

**Moderately**

She loves you, yeah, yeah, yeah. She loves you, yeah,
yeah, yeah. She loves you, yeah, yeah, yeah, yeah.

1. You think you've lost your love? Well, I saw her yes-ter-
(2.) said you hurt her so, she al-most lost her
(3.) know it's up to you, I think it's on-ly

Words & Music by John Lennon & Paul McCartney

© Copyright 1963 Sony/ATV Music Publishing.

All Rights Reserved. International Copyright Secured.

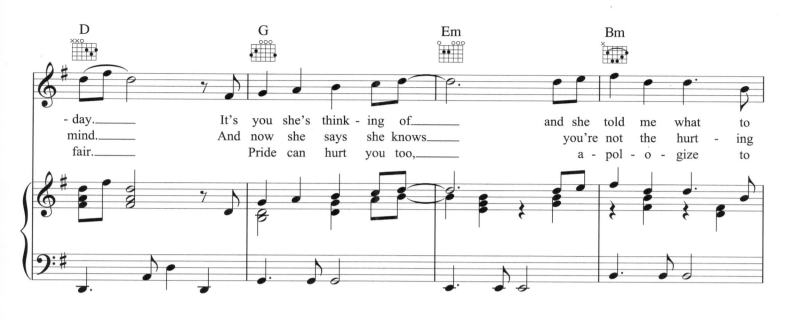

- day._____ It's you she's think - ing of_____ and she told me what to
mind._____ And now she says she knows_____ you're not the hurt - ing
fair._____ Pride can hurt you too,_____ a - pol - o - gize to

say:_____ She says she } loves you and you know that can't be
kind._____ She says she } loves you and you know that can't be
her._____ Be - cause she } loves you and you know that can't be

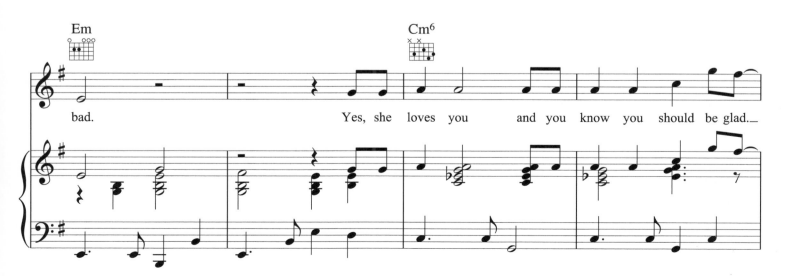

bad. Yes, she loves you and you know you should be glad._____

ADELE 2011

# SOMEONE LIKE YOU

WRITERS: Adele Adkins, Dan Wilson

PRODUCERS: Adele Adkins, Dan Wilson

ALBUM: 21

PEAK POSITION: Number 1 (5 weeks)

WEEKS ON CHART: 64

SALES: 1.36m

Words & Music by Adele Adkins & Daniel Wilson

© Copyright 2010 Universal Music Publishing Limited/Sugar Lake Music/Chrysalis Music Limited.

All Rights Reserved. International Copyright Secured.

WHIGFIELD 1994

# SATURDAY NIGHT

WRITERS: Larry Pignagnoli, Davide Riva

PRODUCER: Larry Pignagnoli

ALBUM: Whigfield

PEAK POSITION: Number 1 (4 weeks)

WEEKS ON CHART: 18

SALES: 1.14m

Sa-tur-day night_ I feel the air is get-ting hot, like you ba-by. I'll make you mine,_ you know I'll take you to the top,

Words & Music by Alfredo Pignagnoli & Davide Riva

© Copyright 1994 Energy Production SRL, Italy.

Universal/MCA Music Limited.

All Rights Reserved. International Copyright Secured.

# TELETUBBIES 1997
# TELETUBBIES SAY "EH-OH!"

WRITERS: Andrew McCrorie-Shand, Andrew Davenport
PRODUCER: Andrew McCrorie-Shand, Steve James
ALBUM: N/A
PEAK POSITION: Number 1 (2 weeks)
WEEKS ON CHART: 32
SALES: 1.11m

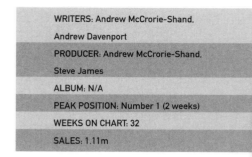

Words by Andrew Davenport
Music by Andrew McCrorie-Shand
© Copyright 1997 Ragdoll Worldwide Limited.
Accorder Music Publishing Ltd.
All Rights Reserved. International Copyright Secured.

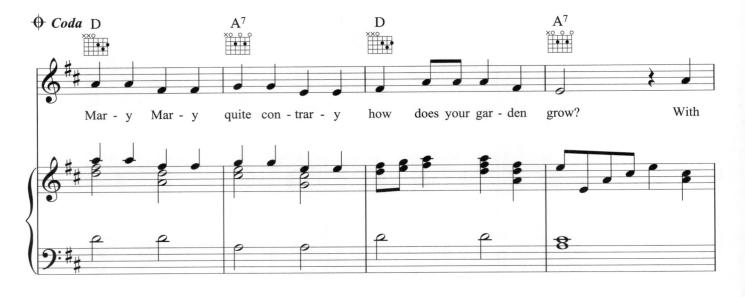

Mar - y Mar - y quite con - trar - y how does your gar - den grow? With

sil - ver bells and cock - le shells and pret - ty maids all in a row.

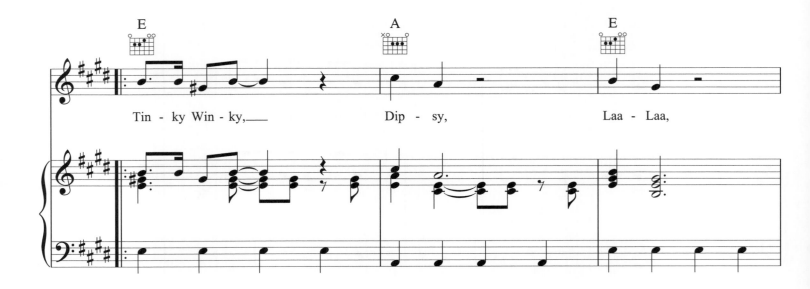

Tin - ky Win - ky,___ Dip - sy, Laa - Laa,

SOFT CELL 1981

WRITER: Ed Cobb

PRODUCER: Mike Thorne

ALBUM: Non-Stop Erotic Cabaret

PEAK POSITION: Number 1 (2 weeks)

WEEKS ON CHART: 44 weeks (1981, 30;

1985, 6; 1991, 8)

SALES: 1.27m

# TAINTED LOVE

**With a moving beat**

Some - times___ I feel___ I've got to

run a - way,___ I've got to get a - way___ from the pain you

drive_ in - to the heart_ of me.___ The love___ we___ share___ seems to

Words & Music by Ed Cobb
© Copyright 1967 Equinox Music.
Campbell Connelly & Company Limited.
All Rights Reserved. International Copyright Secured.

WRITERS: Jörgen Elofsson, Jem Godfrey,
Bill Padley

PRODUCERS: Per Magnusson, David Kreuger

ALBUM: Shayne Ward

PEAK POSITION: Number 1 (4 weeks)

WEEKS ON CHART: 21

SALES: 1.1m

SHAYNE WARD 2005

# THAT'S MY GOAL

Mm.

Yeah,— yeah, yeah.———

1. You know where I

come from,— you know my sto- ry.— You know why I'm

Words & Music by Jörgen Elofsson, Bill Padley & Jeremy Godfrey
© Copyright 2005 Universal Music Publishing Limited/Universal Music Publishing MGB Limited.
All Rights Reserved. International Copyright Secured.

**CELINE DION** 1994
# THINK TWICE

WRITERS: Andy Hill, Peter Sinfield
PRODUCERS: Christopher Neil, Aldo Nova
ALBUM: The Colour Of My Love
PEAK POSITION: Number 1 (7 weeks)
WEEKS ON CHART: 31
SALES: 1.3m

1. Don't think I can't feel that there's some-thing wrong,

(2.) twice, for the sake of our love for the mem-o-ry,

you've been the sweet-est part of my life for so long.
for the fire and the faith that was you and me.

Words & Music by Andy Hill & Pete Sinfield
© Copyright 1993 Chrysalis Music Limited/Imagem London Limited.
All Rights Reserved. International Copyright Secured.

WRITERS: an Broudie, David Baddiel, Frank Skinner

PRODUCERS: Ian Broudie, Simon Rogers, Dave Bascombe

ALBUM: N/A

PEAK POSITION: Number 1 (2 weeks)

WEEKS ON CHART: 46 (1996, 15: 1998, 13: 2002, 6: 2006, 6: 2010, 6)

SALES: 1.53m

BADDIEL & SKINNER & LIGHTNING SEEDS 1996

# THREE LIONS

Words by David Baddiel & Frank Skinner

Music by Ian Broudie

© Copyright 1996 Avalon Management Group Limited/Chrysalis Music Limited.

All Rights Reserved. International Copyright Secured.

# THE RIGHTEOUS BROTHERS 1965
# UNCHAINED MELODY

WRITERS: Alex North (music), Hy Zaret (lyrics)
PRODUCER: Phil Spector
ALBUM: N/A
PEAK POSITION: Number 1 (4 weeks)
WEEKS ON CHART: 26 (1965, 12; 1990, 14)
SALES: 1.04m

Oh_____ my_____ love,_____ my__ darl - ing,_____ I've hun - gered for your__ touch a long lone - ly

Words by Hy Zaret
Music by Alex North

© Copyright 1954 (Renewed 1982) Frank Music Corporation, USA.
MPL Communications Limited.
All Rights Reserved. International Copyright Secured.

SPICE GIRLS 1996
# WANNABE

WRITERS: Matthew Rowbottom,
Richard Stannard, Spice Girls
PRODUCERS: Matthew Rowbottom,
Richard Stannard
ALBUM: Spice
PEAK POSITION: Number 1 (7 weeks)
WEEKS ON CHART: 26
SALES: 1.32m

Words & Music by Matt Rowe, Richard Stannard, Melanie Brown, Victoria Adams, Geri Halliwell, Emma Bunton & Melanie Chisholm
© Copyright 1996 Universal Music Publishing Limited (administered in Germany by Universal Music Publ. GmbH)/EMI Music Publishing (WP) Limited.
All Rights Reserved. International Copyright Secured.

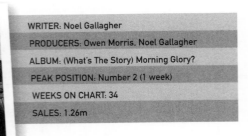

WRITER: Noel Gallagher

PRODUCERS: Owen Morris, Noel Gallagher

ALBUM: (What's The Story) Morning Glory?

PEAK POSITION: Number 2 (1 week)

WEEKS ON CHART: 34

SALES: 1.26m

OASIS 1995

# WONDERWALL

To - day is gon - na be the day that they're gon - na throw it back to you,___

by now you should-'ve some - how re - al - ised what you got - ta do.___

Words & Music by Noel Gallagher

© Copyright 1995 Creation Songs Limited/Oasis Music (GB).

Sony/ATV Music Publishing.

All Rights Reserved. International Copyright Secured.

# Y.M.C.A.

WRITERS: Henri Belolo, Jacques Morali, Victor Willis

PRODUCER: Jacques Morali

ALBUM: Cruisin'

PEAK POSITION: Number 1 (3 weeks)

WEEKS ON CHART: 26 (1978, 16; 1993, 7; 1999, 3)

SALES: 1.46m

**Disco** ♩ = 136

*play 4 times*

1. Young man, there's no
2. Young man, there's a
*(Verses 3-6 see block lyrics)*

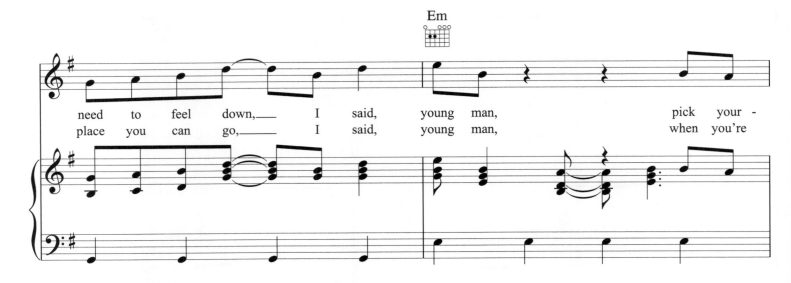

need to feel down,___ I said, young man, pick your-
place you can go,___ I said, young man, when you're

Words & Music by Jacques Morali, Henri Belolo & Victor Willis

© Copyright 1978 Scorpio Music Sarl, France

EMI Music Publishing Limited

All Rights Reserved. International Copyright Secured.

*Verse 3:*

Young man, are you listening to me?
I said, young man what do you want to be?
I said, young man you can make real your dreams
But you've got to know this one thing.

*Verse 4:*

No man does it all by himself.
I said young man put your pride on the shelf.
And just go there to the Y.M.C.A.
I'm sure they can help you today.
*Chorus*

*Verse 5:*

Young man I was once in your shoes
I said, I was down and out and with the blues.
I felt no man cared if I were alive.
I felt the whole world was so jive.

*Verse 6:*

That's when someone come up to me
And said, "Young man, take a walk up the street.
It's a place there called the Y.M.C.A.
They can start you back on your way."
*Chorus*

WRITER: John Farrar

PRODUCER: John Farrar

ALBUM: Grease (soundtrack)

PEAK POSITION: Number 1 (9 weeks)

WEEKS ON CHART: 35 (1978, 26; 1998, 9)

SALES: 2m

JOHN TRAVOLTA & OLIVIA NEWTON-JOHN 1978

# YOU'RE THE ONE THAT I WANT

Words & Music by John Farrar

© Copyright 1978 Ensign Music Corporation, USA/Sony/ATV Music Publishing LLC/Stigwood Music, Inc./John Farrar Music, Inc.

Famous Music Corporation.

All Rights Reserved. International Copyright Secured.

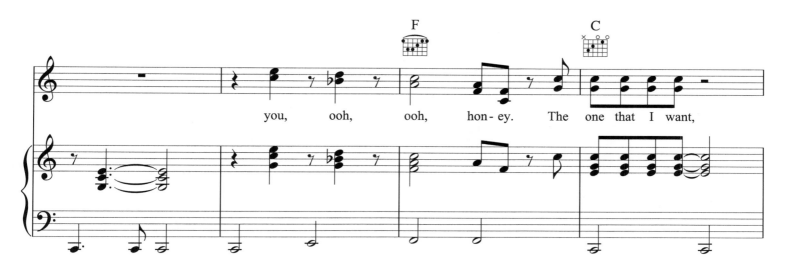

you, ooh, ooh, hon- ey. The one that I want,

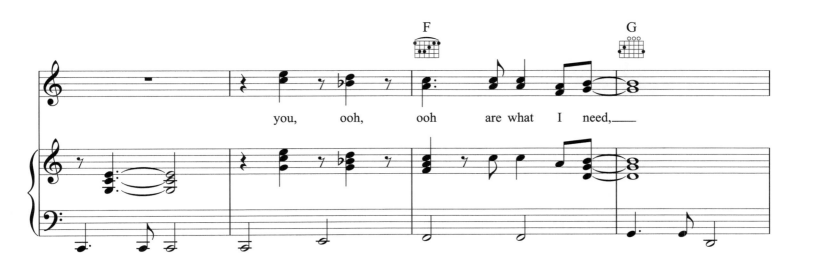

you, ooh, ooh are what I need,____

oh yes in - deed. 2. *(Female)* If you're You're the

If you enjoyed this playing the music from this book, you may also
be interested in reading the complete book edition from Omnibus Press

# THE MILLION SELLERS

## Book Edition

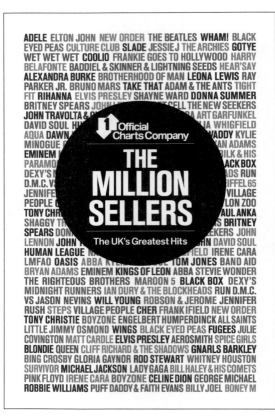

Published to mark the 60th anniversary of the launch of the
Official Singles Charts in 1952, The Million Sellers tells the story
of every million-selling single in the history of the UK music
industry. An analysis of the 123 singles which have passed the
magical million sales threshold in the UK in the past 60 years,
from Bill Haley & The Comets' very first UK million seller right
through to more recent singles by Lady Gaga, Rihanna and the
Black Eyed Peas.

Interviews with artists like Mel C, Kevin Rowland and Midge
Ure, reflecting on their own million seller and what they most
remember of their success at the time.

Interviews with artists including Engelbert Humperdinck,
Steps, Bernard Sumner (New Order), Midge Ure (Ultravox),
Mel C (Spice Girls), Boney M, Kevin Rowland and many more.
Each one reflects on their own million seller and what they
most remember of their success at the time.

The Official Charts Company are the providers of the UK's only official music and video charts, compiling its
charts purely from sales information gathered across all key distribution (or entertainment) channels including
all major high street retail chains, independent stores, supermarkets, mail order internet retailers and digital
music service providers. This market research sample equates to 99% of the total UK singles market; 98% of
the total UK albums market and 90% of the total UK DVD market.

The Official Charts Company is a joint venture between record labels' body the BPI and ERA, the Entertainment
Retailers Association. The Official Charts Company are responsible for the commissioning, marketing,
distribution and management of the UK's industry standard music charts and industry sales data.

Available from all good music shops & **www.musicroom.com**

Order No. : OP54956
ISBN: 978.1.78038.718.5